Problems in Plant Physiology

M. K. Sands

Problems in Plant Physiology

John Murray Albemarle Street London

Printed in Hong Kong
by King's Time Printing Press Ltd.

0 7195 2318 4

Acknowledgments

I am grateful to the following authors and publishers who have allowed me to make use of their material.

Figs. 5, 7, 11, 15: from Fogg, G. E. (1968), *Photosynthesis*, Figs. 14, 13, 39, Plate 11a. English Universities Press.

Fig. 6: after Strasburger's *Textbook of Botany*, New English Edition (1965), Fig. 312. Longmans.

Fig. 9: after Ashby, M. (1961), *Introduction to Plant Ecology*, Fig. 4.1. Macmillan and Co., London.

Fig. 10: redrawn after Evans, L. T. (1968), 'Photosynthesis under Natural Conditions', *Penguin Science Survey* 1968: *Biology*, Fig. 21. Penguin Books Ltd.

Fig. 12: after Ray, P. M. (1963), *The Living Plant*, Fig. 3-1. Holt, Rinehart and Winston, Inc.

Figs. 13, 14: after Bassham, J. A. (1959), 'Photosynthesis', Figs. 6 and 7, *J. Chem. Ed.*, **36**, 548-554.

Page 16: table from Westlake, D. F. (1963), 'Comparisons of Plant Productivity', Table 2, *Biol. Rev.* **38**, 385-425.

Page 17: tables on yield of beet from University of Bristol Department of Economics.

Figs. 22, 53: from Fogg, G. E. (1963), *The Growth of Plants*, Figs. 48 and 25. Penguin Books Ltd.

Fig. 25: from Odum, E. P. (1959), *Fundamentals of Ecology*, Fig. 90. W. B. Saunders Company Ltd.

Fig. 26: from Baron, W. M. M. (1967), *Water and Plant Life*, Fig. 4.7. Heinemann. Redrawn after data of Martin, E. V. 'Studies of evaporation and transpiration under controlled conditions', *Carnegie Inst. Wash. Publ.* **550** (Washington, 1943).

Fig. 28: from Baron, W. M. M. (1967), *Water and Plant Life*, Fig. 4.9. Heinemann. Redrawn after Meyer, B. S. and Anderson, D. B., *Plant Physiology*, Van Nostrand, New York, 1952.

Fig. 30: after Noel, A. R. A. (1959), 'Some New Techniques in Plant Physiology' Fig. 2, *School Science Review*, **142**, 496-502. John Murray.

Figs. 35, 36, 38: Photographs by John Haller, Harris Biological Supplies.

Fig. 39: from Baron, W. M. M. (1963), *Organisation in Plants*, Fig. 2.7. Edward Arnold Ltd.

Fig. 42: from Smithers, A. G. and Wilson, K. (1968), 'Laboratory Investigations in Plant Physiology', Fig. 2, *J. Biol. Ed.* **2**, no. 3.

vi Acknowledgments

Page 44: table and Fig. 45 from Stout, P. R. and Hoagland, D. R. (1939), 'Upward and lateral movement of salt in certain plants as indicated by radioactive isotopes of K, Na and P absorbed by roots', Table 1, and redrawn from Fig. 1a, *Am. J. Bot.* **26**, 320-324.

Page 45: table from Biddulph, O. and Markle, J. (1944), 'Translocation of radio phosphorus in the phloem of the cotton plant', Table 2, *Am. J. Bot.*, **31**, 65-70.

Fig. 46: photograph by Dr A. J. Peel, Department of Botany, University of Hull.

Fig. 48: after Postlethwait, S. N. and Rogers, B. (1958), *Am. J. Bot.*, **45**, 753-757.

Fig. 60: from James, W. O. (1963), *An Introduction to Plant Physiology*, 6th edn., Fig. 66.   Oxford University Press.

Fig. 65: from Luckwill, L. C. (1953), 'Studies in fruit development in relation to plant hormones', Fig. 3, *J. hort. Sci.* **28**, 14-24.

I wish to record my thanks to Mr S. W. Hurry and Mr D. G. Mackean who not only commented on the problems, but also tried them out with their sixth form students.

Contents

3 Water Relations

4 Translocation

5 Respiration

6 Plant Hormones

Problems in Plant Physiology

1 Photosynthesis

1.1 The effect of external factors on the rate of photosynthesis

The rate of photosynthesis at different light intensities was determined for a plant. The results are shown in Fig. 1.

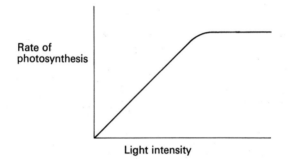

Fig. 1. **Photosynthesis and light intensity.**

1 What is the relationship between photosynthesis and light intensity?

The results in Fig. 1 were obtained in ordinary air, which has a carbon dioxide concentration of 0.03%. If the air is enriched with extra carbon dioxide and the rate of photosynthesis in a constant light intensity measured, a graph such as that shown in Fig. 2 is obtained.

2 At the highest light intensities in Fig. 1 the rate of photosynthesis is not increasing. From Fig. 2 suggest one factor which could be limiting the process.

3 Fig. 3 shows the relation of photosynthesis to another external factor, temperature. Comment on the relationship between photosynthesis and temperature.

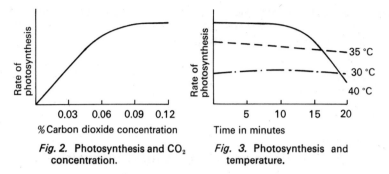

Fig. 2. Photosynthesis and CO_2 concentration.

Fig. 3. Photosynthesis and temperature.

Figure 4 shows the interaction of the three factors discussed above.

4 Analyse Fig. 4 in the following way:

a Make a general statement about the relationship between the rate of photosynthesis and light intensity.

b For curve 1 put into words the relationship between the rate of photosynthesis, light intensity and temperature.

c In curve 1 which factor seems to be limiting the rate?

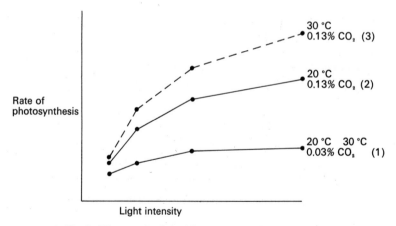

Fig. 4. Photosynthesis and light intensity, CO_2 concentration and temperature.

5 The rate of photosynthesis depends to a large extent on the external factors of light, carbon dioxide, and temperature. Write a few sentences describing the relationship between these three factors and the rate of photosynthesis as far as you can understand it from the data provided here.

6 Each of these three factors will limit the rate of photosynthesis under different environmental conditions. In which ecological situations would you expect the limiting factor to be

a light

b carbon dioxide

c temperature?

1.2 Adaptations to different light intensities

A Fig. 5 shows the rate of photosynthesis (as photosynthesis relative to a maximum of 100), in relation to light intensity, of phytoplankton taken from three depths in the Sargasso Sea. Curve A is for phytoplankton at the surface receiving 100% of the available light. Curves B and C are for phytoplankton to which 10% and 1% respectively of the surface light penetrates.

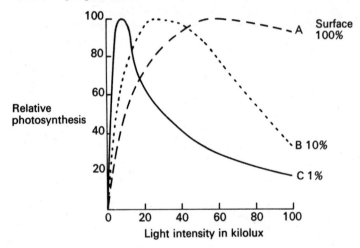

Fig. 5. Light intensity and photosynthesis in phytoplankton.

1 Assuming that the constitution of each of the three populations of phytoplankton is similar, account for the difference in the three curves in Fig. 5.

2 Compare the two populations depicted in curves A and C of Fig. 5 with the sun and shade plants shown in Fig. 6.

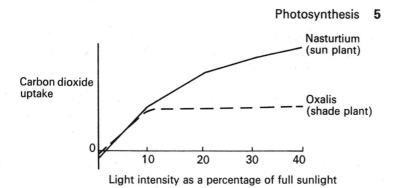

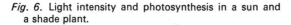

Fig. 6. Light intensity and photosynthesis in a sun and a shade plant.

B The amount of chlorophyll in plants can be made to vary by growing in high or low light intensities. Those grown in a high light intensity have a lower chlorophyll content than those grown in a low light intensity. The light intensity at which the highest relative photosynthesis is achieved is termed the saturation intensity. The green alga, *Chlorella*, was grown in low and high intensity light in dilute culture to avoid much self-shading. The curves relating the rate of photosynthesis per cell to light intensity are shown in Fig. 7.

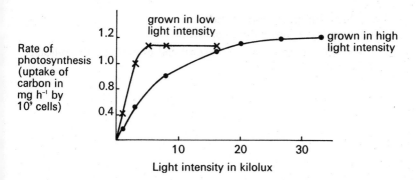

Fig. 7. Light intensity and photosynthesis of *Chlorella*.

3 a Which culture was the more efficient at low light intensity?
  b Which culture reached saturation intensity first?

6   Photosynthesis

C   Fig. 8 gives the area of two leaves of the same species measured during their growth.   Leaf A was grown at a high light intensity and Leaf B at a low light intensity.

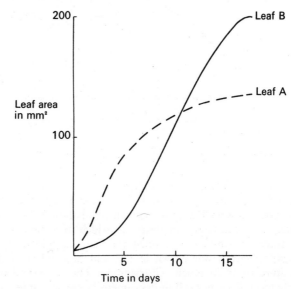

Fig. 8. Leaf areas of leaves grown at two light intensities.

4 a Which leaf grows faster at first?
 b Which leaf achieves the larger area?

5 Comment on the possible ecological and physiological significance of the data in Figs. 7 and 8.

1.3   Compensation point

Plants photosynthesise in daylight hours only, but respire both day and night.   They take in carbon dioxide during photosynthesis, and release carbon dioxide during respiration.   The point at which carbon dioxide uptake in photosynthesis equals carbon dioxide output in respiration is called the *compensation point*.

In a woodland community the trees are usually sun plants, adapted to a high light intensity.   Their seedlings are often capable, as in the oak, of tolerating shade conditions.   The shade plants usually reach their compensation point at a lower light intensity than the sun plants. The compensation point for the former may be as low as 0.3 to 1.0% of maximum daylight, as compared with 1.3 to 7.5% for sun plants. This is shown diagrammatically in Fig. 9.

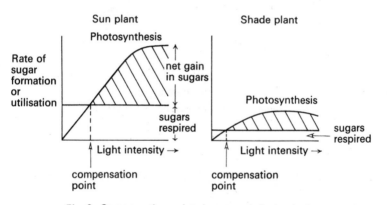

Fig. 9. Compensation points in sun and shade plants.

1   Comment on the ecological significance of the different compensation points for sun and shade plants.

2   The utilisation of carbon dioxide in photosynthesis is much less temperature sensitive than the production of carbon dioxide in respiration.   This fact has important bearings on glasshouse management.   In seasons of low light intensity it is essential to keep temperatures at the safe minimum for the crop concerned.

a Explain why it is essential to do this.

b How could the safe minimum temperature be defined?

1.4 Adaptation to latitude

Fig. 10 shows the effect of temperature on the rate of photosynthesis of a temperate grass (ryegrass) and a subtropical grass (*Paspalum*). The graphs shown are typical of a large number of temperate and subtropical plants.

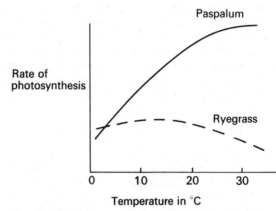

Fig. 10. Temperature and photosynthesis in two grasses.

1 Name two features of the environment which differ in tropical and temperate regions.

2 State how temperature affects the rate of photosynthesis of the two species shown in Fig. 10.

3 What is the ecological significance of the different relationships to temperature and photosynthesis possessed by the two species?

1.5 The chloroplast and photosynthesis

T. W. Engelman in 1883 performed a series of ingenious experiments to investigate the part played by chlorophyll in photosynthesis. He used bacteria which migrated towards oxygen as an indication that photosynthesis was taking place.

1 How would the migration of these bacteria demonstrate photosynthesis?

Some of Engelman's results are shown in Fig. 11.

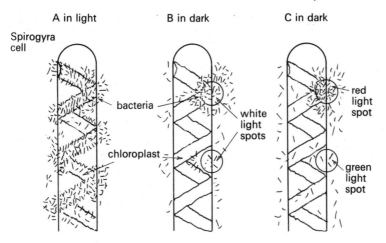

Fig. 11. Engelman's experiments on the part played by chlorophyll in photosynthesis.

2 What does the congregation of bacteria around the chloroplast in A show?

3 B showed that bacteria congregated around a spot of white light shining through the chloroplast, but not around a spot shining through the cytoplasm. One hypothesis to explain this could be simply that the bacteria are attracted to green light (i.e. white light shining through a chloroplast) but not to white light. How does C refute this hypothesis?

1.6 Pigments, wavelengths and photosynthesis

In order to have a photochemical effect, light must be *absorbed* rather than transmitted or reflected. The substances responsible in most higher plants for absorption in photosynthesis are the pigments present in the chloroplast: chlorophyll a, chlorophyll b, and the 2 yellow carotenoids, carotene and xanthophyll (now known as lutein).

All four pigments absorb light, but of particular wavelengths only. The chlorophylls have maximum absorption in the blue-violet, and red, and the carotenoids in the blue-violet range.

The range of impinging light absorbed by a green plant, or by a solution of chlorophyll, can be measured for each wavelength using a spectrophotometer. The results give a curve called an *absorption spectrum*, which is characteristic for any coloured compound.

If a green plant is illuminated by equally intense beams of light of a succession of different wavelengths, the rate of photosynthesis at each can be measured. The results give an *action spectrum* for photosynthesis as shown in Fig. 12.

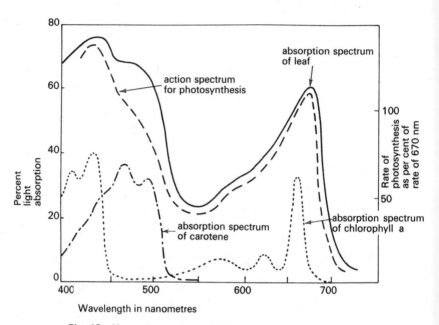

Fig. 12. Absorption spectra of chlorophyll pigments, and action spectrum for photosynthesis.

1 What relationship is there between the action spectrum for photosynthesis and the absorption spectrum of the leaf?

2 What conclusions can you draw about photosynthesis and light absorption by chlorophyll?

1.7 The conversion of carbon dioxide in photosynthesis

To determine the path of carbon dioxide in photosynthesis a unicellular alga such as *Chlorella* or *Scenedesmus* may be used. When the algae are actively photosynthesising radioactive carbon dioxide ($^{14}CO_2$) is supplied. The algae can be run out of the apparatus at any time into a tube containing methanol, which immediately kills them, and gives an extract of the substances formed in them. The extract can then be examined by chromatographic techniques and the labelled compounds identified.

1 a Why are unicellular algae preferable to green leaves for this work?
  b Why is radioactive carbon dioxide used?
  c What assumption is made in using radioactive tracers?

Our knowledge of the conversion of carbon dioxide is mainly due to the work of Melvin Calvin and his group at the University of California at Berkeley, for which he received the Nobel prize in 1961. Calvin found that the carbon dioxide is first combined with a carbohydrate molecule containing five carbon atoms, ribulose diphosphate (RDP). The product of this reaction immediately splits into two molecules of a 3 carbon compound, phosphoglyceric acid (PGA). PGA is then reduced, probably by $NADPH_2$, to a triose phosphate, a 3 carbon sugar.

This problem is concerned only with some of the evidence which indicated that carbon dioxide and RDP produce two molecules of PGA. Fig. 13 shows what happens to PGA and RDP in the light and dark, and Fig. 14 what happens when the level of carbon dioxide around the photosynthesising cells is reduced.

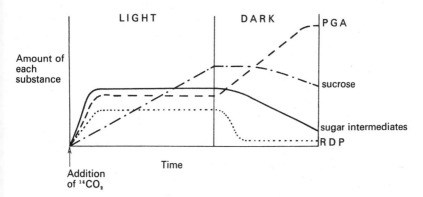

Fig. 13. Accumulation and loss of photosynthetic products in light and dark. (After Bassham, J.A. (1959), 'Photosynthesis', Fig. 6, *J. Chem Ed.*, **36**, 548-554.)

2 How does Fig. 13 indicate that

  a both RDP and PGA are being formed in photosynthesis
  b RDP is being utilised in the dark
  c PGA is being formed from RDP
  d other materials are possibly involved in the cycle, but not so closely tied to either PGA or RDP?

3 Explain why, in Fig. 14, the level of RDP rises when the amount of carbon dioxide is reduced.

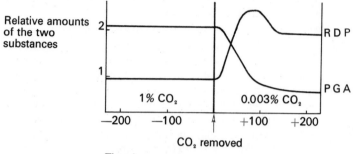

Fig. 14. The relative amounts of PGA and RDP at two levels of carbon dixoide. (After Bassham, J.A. (1959), 'Photosynthesis', Fig. 7, *J. Chem Ed.*, **36**, 548-554.)

4 RDP when added to photosynthesising algae stimulates the uptake of carbon dioxide and the production of PGA. How does this further fact support the above stated path of carbon dioxide?

1.8   The source of ATP in photosynthesis

Leaf discs from a destarched plant were placed either in water or in a glucose solution.   Half of those in water and half of those in glucose were exposed to air enriched with carbon dioxide, the other half were kept in an atmosphere of nitrogen enriched with carbon dioxide.   For 24 hours all leaf discs in their respective flasks were kept at 20 °C, but half were placed in the light and the remainder in the dark.

At the end of 24 hours the leaf discs were tested for starch.   The results are shown in the table.

	Glucose		Water	
	In air with CO_2	In nitrogen with CO_2	In air with CO_2	In nitrogen with CO_2
Light	S	S	S	S
Dark	S	NS	NS	NS

S = starch present   NS = starch not present

STARCH CONTENT OF LEAF DISCS KEPT IN VARIOUS CONDITIONS

This experiment supports the hypothesis that the ATP required in the process of starch formation can come from one of two sources:

a the aerobic respiration of glucose, where oxygen is necessary but not light,

b photophosphorylation, where light is necessary but not oxygen.

For each of the positive results above state which of the two sources a or b could be a possible source of ATP.

1.9   Photosynthesis and respiration

The two processes of photosynthesis and respiration have many common enzymes and intermediate products. In addition the end products of one are the starting materials for the other. One would imagine that there are many possibilities for interactions between the two processes. The intermediates, however, do not necessarily exist in a common pool within the cell. The two organelles concerned with photosynthesis and respiration (chloroplasts and mitochondria respectively) are usually quite distinct in most cells, and interchange between them may be slight.

In photosynthesis studies, therefore, the assumption is usually made that respiration proceeds at the same rate in both light and dark, and is independent of photosynthesis. The rate of photosynthesis which is actually measured would be the *net* rate. This is presumably less than the gross or actual rate by the amount the plant has respired. To give the actual rate a correction has to be made to the net rate. For example, if photosynthesis is measured as oxygen production, the amount of oxygen used by the same plant in respiration in the dark (but in otherwise similar conditions) is added on to the amount of oxygen produced during an equal period in the light.

The use of the heavy oxygen isotope, ^{18}O, has enabled this assumption to be tested. Fig. 15 shows changes in amounts of oxygen of different mass (examined in a mass spectrometer) around a tobacco leaf which was supplied with oxygen containing both normal ($^{16}O_2$) and heavy oxygen ($^{18}O_2$).

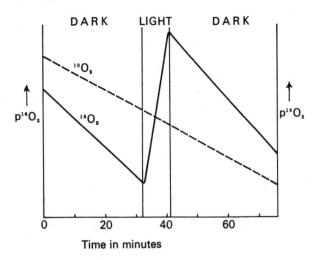

Fig. 15. Oxygen in respiration and photosynthesis.

1   Were both types of oxygen used in equal amounts in respiration?

2   Is the assumption that respiration proceeds at the same rate in light and dark justified from these results?

3   Which type of oxygen was given out in photosynthesis?

4   If the oxygen given out in photosynthesis had come from the oxygen around the plant, one would have expected a similar increase in the amount of both types of oxygen during the light period. This did not happen.   From which compound or compounds used in photosynthesis could the oxygen produced by the process have come?

Ruben, in 1940, using the same technique, identified the source of oxygen produced in photosynthesis.   Plants were supplied with either ^{18}O enriched water $H_2{}^{18}O$, or ^{18}O enriched carbon dioxide $C^{18}O_2$. When given $C^{18}O_2$, no heavy oxygen was produced in photosynthesis. When given $H_2{}^{18}O$ the percentage of heavy oxygen in the oxygen produced varied with the percentage of $H_2{}^{18}O$ in the water used.

5   What conclusions do you draw as to the source of the oxygen produced in photosynthesis?

1.10   Carbon dioxide uptake and release

The net amount of carbon dioxide taken in by a plant in the light, and the amount of carbon dioxide produced in the dark were determined at different temperatures.   The results are given in the table.

Temperature °C:	5	10	15	20	25	30
Net uptake of CO_2 in light	1.1	2.2	2.8	3.1	2.8	2.0
Release of CO_2 in dark	0.2	0.5	0.8	1.1	1.7	2.4

UPTAKE AND RELEASE OF CARBON DIXOIDE (mg CO_2 PER g DRY WEIGHT PER HOUR)

1   What would you expect to happen to the amount of carbon dioxide around this plant if it were

a   photosynthesising under a bell jar
b   placed under a bell jar in the dark?

2   Assume that, for the plant depicted in the table, the rate of respiration in the light is equal to that in the dark.   Calculate its true uptake of carbon dioxide in photosynthesis.

3   How are respiration and true and apparent photosynthesis related to temperature?   You will need to graph true and apparent uptake, and loss, of carbon dioxide.

1.11   Yields of natural vegetation and crops in photosynthesis

	Annual production in tonnes of organic matter per hectare year	Average daily production in growing season in grammes of carbon fixed per day
Sugar cane, Java	87	11.0
Maize crop, Minnesota	24	8.1
Tropical rain forest	59	7.6
Marsh, Minnesota	23	6.0
Beet, Holland	17	5.0
Sublittoral seaweed, Nova Scotia	32	3.9
Littoral seaweed, Nova Scotia (dry between tides)	18.5	2.5
Birch forest, England	8.5	2.2
Pine forest, England	16	2.0
Arctic tundra	1	very small

ANNUAL PRODUCTION (COLUMN 1) OF DIFFERENT TYPES OF VEGETATION AND THEIR AVERAGE DAILY PRODUCTION (COLUMN 2) IN THE GROWING SEASON. (PRODUCTION MEANS THE NET AMOUNT OF NEW TISSUE MADE.)

1   Considering all the types of vegetation listed, the table shows that there is more variation in annual production than in the average daily growing season production of photosynthesis. It also shows that in the same climate (England) the annual production of an evergreen forest is greater than that of a deciduous forest.
Give one hypothesis which would account for both

   a the greater variation in annual production than in daily production, and

   b the difference in annual production between evergreen and deciduous forest.

2   Compare arctic and tropical vegetation. What ecological differences might account for differences in

   a average daily production,
   b annual production?

3 a Which are the 5 communities with the highest annual production?
   b Have these communities anything in common which would account for their high production?
   c Explain the difference in production between littoral and sublittoral seaweed in the same terms.

4   How does the average daily production of cultivated crops compare with that of natural vegetation?

5   One way of obtaining the figures given in the table is to harvest samples of the aerial part of the plants at the end of the growing season, and determine the dry mass. In what ways does this method give an incomplete picture of production during photosynthesis?

1.12   Crop yield

So many factors are involved in the growth and harvesting of a crop that it is often difficult to account exactly for a good or a bad crop yield. Many agricultural research units and university departments of agriculture assist the farmer by carrying out carefully controlled experiments to investigate the effect of different conditions on crop plant growth.

Some of the results of such an investigation, involving the cooperation of a large number of farmers, are given in the tables below.

Sowing period	Yield in tonnes per hectare
On or before March 20	30.6
March 21-31	31.4
April 1-14	38
April 15-30	34.6
May 1-14	27.7
After May 14	23.9

DATE OF SOWING AND LATER YIELD OF BEET

Average plant population in thousands per hectare	Yield in tonnes per hectare
5.4	29
65.9	34.9
76.5	41.6

PLANT DENSITY AND LATER YIELD OF BEET

1   Comment on the relationship between
   a date of sowing and yield,
   b density and yield.
2   Why would you expect the date the beet was sown to have an effect on its yield at harvest?
3   Give the advantages and disadvantages for the farmer of growing crops at high densities.

2 Germination and Growth

2.1 Seed dormancy

Seed dormancy may be due to (i) the external conditions of the environment, such as lack of water, low temperature, lack of oxygen, presence or absence of light; or (ii) the structure or physiology of the seed.

The following is a list of observations relating to dormancy caused by the second set of conditions: the seed structure and physiology.

a Some seeds will not germinate until the testa is broken. This may be done artificially by scratching or cutting the testa, or naturally by the action of micro-organisms or the seasonal changes within the soil.

b Some seeds such as those of orchids are shed while the embryo is still immature and they will not germinate immediately.

c In many species chemicals inhibiting germination are produced. The source of the chemical may be the fleshy part of the fruit, thus preventing germination inside the fruit; the leaves, thus preventing germination in the leaf litter under the plant; or the seed itself.

d In a number of species with seeds containing a mature embryo or possessing a permeable testa, such as the sycamore, germination will not occur until the seed has been exposed for a period to temperatures just above freezing. It is in the embryo and not any other part of the seed that these changes, called 'after-ripening', occur.

1 From the above

  a summarise the internal causes of dormancy,

  b say how, in your opinion, each of the four points mentioned could cause dormancy.

2 Discuss the biological significance of dormancy caused either by external or internal factors.

2.2   Changes on germination

A number of ungerminated hemp seeds were analysed to discover the amounts of protein, fat, starch, cellulose, other organic substances, and inorganic constituents present.   Similar analyses were done on equal numbers of seedlings six and nine days after germination.   The results of the analyses are given in the table, as percentages.

	Fat	Protein	Starch	Cellulose	Other organic substances	Inorganic substances	Loss in weight
Seeds	33	24	0	15	23	5	—
6-day-old seedlings	18	23	7	15·1	28	5	3·9
9-day-old seedlings	16	23·5	3	16·6	29	5	6·9

CHANGES IN THE CONSTITUTION OF SEEDS AND SEEDLINGS DURING GERMINATION. THE FIGURES ARE PERCENTAGES.

Discuss the changes which took place during germination.

2.3   Germination in light and dark

Two samples of mung bean seeds were grown in identical conditions except that one sample was in the dark, the other in daylight. After 15 days and after 25 days the same number of plants was removed from each sample and the average fresh and dry mass found. In addition, the average fresh and dry mass of the same number of mung bean seeds were found. The changes in mass under both dark and light conditions are shown in Fig. 16.

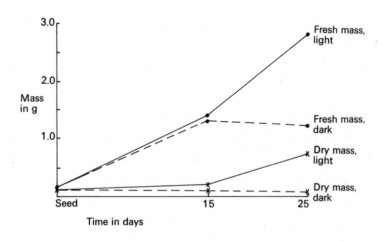

Fig. 16.   Mass of mung bean seedlings germinated in light and dark.

1   Explain these results by commenting on

   a   the increase in fresh mass of the plants in the light; and this compared with the fresh mass increase of the plants in the dark,

   b   the difference in wet and dry mass of the seed,

   c   the changes in dry mass in the light; and this compared with the dry mass decrease in the dark.

2   List the advantages and disadvantages of using both dry and fresh mass as a measure of plant growth.

2.4   Growth curves

Fig. 17 shows the curve which is usually obtained when the growth of an organism is plotted (as size or mass of the whole organism or of part of it) against time.   In general terms the curve shows three stages of growth: (1) starting slowly, (2) gradually becoming faster, and (3) finally slowing down again.   There may also be a fourth stage (4) where the organism loses mass.

1   Assume that the organism for which Fig. 17 was drawn was an annual plant.   What do you think is happening to the plant at each of these four stages?

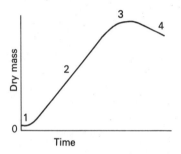

Fig. 17.   Stages of growth of an organism.

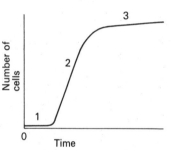
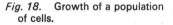

Fig. 18.   Growth of a population of cells.

A similar curve (Fig. 18) is obtained when the growth of a population of cells such as *Chlorella* or bacteria is plotted against time.   The parts of the curve are called:

1. lag phase
2. logarithmic or exponential phase
3. stationary phase.

2   Imagine that this curve represents the growth of a population of bacteria in a flask of nutrient material inoculated with a few bacteria. What do you think would be happening in

a the lag phase
b the exponential phase
c the stationary phase?

3   Imagine that the curve represents the growth of a population of a pathogenic bacterium in the blood of a man.   Which stage in growth do you think would cause high temperatures in the patient?

C

2.5   Growth of three organisms

The tables below give figures for the growth of three organisms.

Day	Mass in g
1	2.8
3	4.1
5	5.9
7	8.9
9	17.9
11	32.0
13	42.0
15	48.0
17	49.5
19	50.1
21	50.1

THE MASS OF A FRUIT MEA-
SURED EVERY TWO DAYS
FROM THE WITHERING OF
THE PETALS TO FINAL
MATURITY

Month	Mass in kg
0 (on hatching)	0.01
1	0.14
2	0.45
3	0.77
4	1.18
5	1.63
6	2.08
7	2.49
8	2.85
9	2.94

THE MASS OF A CHICKEN
MEASURED MONTHLY FROM
TIME OF HATCHING TO
MATURITY

THE HEIGHT OF A STEM OF
MAIZE MEASURED FROM ITS
APPEARANCE ABOVE GROUND

Week	Height in cm
1	3
2	7
3	23
4	40
5	61
6	81
7	101
8	120
9	130
10	138
11	141
12	142

1   Draw a graph for each set of data.

2   Compare and contrast the three curves, and account for the differences between them as far as you can.

2.6   Potato growth

Fig. 19 graphs the dry mass of potato stems, leaves and tubers for
eight weeks after the tuber sprouted.

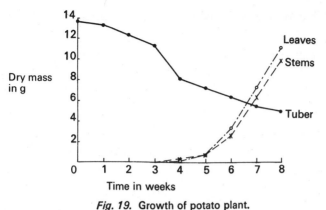

Fig. 19. Growth of potato plant.

1   Explain the phases of growth of the new potato plant.

2   What is the relationship between the tuber and its loss in mass and the gains in leaves and stems?

2.7   Root growth

A number of thick sections were cut from broad bean roots. The number of cells per section and the average volume, dry weight, and respiration rate per cell were found. The results are shown as four graphs, each drawn to a different vertical scale, in Fig. 20.

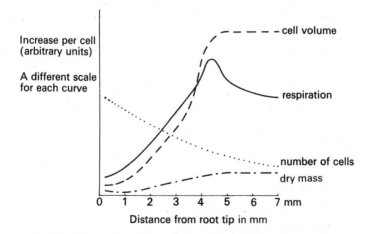

Fig. 20. Changes in cells at different distances from the root tip.

Comment on these graphs.

2.8 Plant growth over twelve weeks

The curves, all three drawn to different vertical scales, shown in Fig. 21 represent the changes in dry mass, height and fresh mass for a species of plant over 12 weeks.

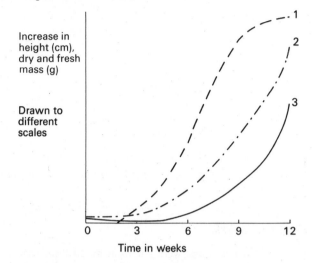

Increase in height (cm), dry and fresh mass (g)

Drawn to different scales

Time in weeks

Fig. 21. Dry mass, height, fresh mass, for a plant over 12 weeks.

1 Choose, with reasons, one curve for each process.

2 How would you expect the three curves to differ from those shown in Fig. 21 if the plant had been grown in the dark?

2.9 Measurement of growth

Growth can be defined as an increase in size. The following criteria may be used to measure growth in plants, animals or both:

a Height	**d** Fresh mass
b Volume	**e** Leaf area
c Dry mass	**f** Organ size

1 What are the merits and demerits of using each of these criteria to measure growth?

2 What criteria would you use to measure the growth of

a a population of bacteria
b a human being
c a crop plant
d a tree?

2.10   Environmental factors affecting growth

The growth of a plant depends on a number of interrelated processes, all of which may respond differently to environmental factors. The processes involved are the uptake of water and salts, photosynthesis, the formation of cytoplasm, cell division and differentiation, and the formation and development of organs.

The environmental factors often have complex and indirect effects: for example, rain will increase the soil water content, and also affect its aeration and the humidity of the air. In addition, there may be complex interrelations between the environment and processes inside the plant: for example, temperature affects humidity which affects the rate of transpiration and can indirectly affect photosynthesis by the closure of the stomata.

The daily growth of a plant shows variations reflecting the effect of different environmental factors. Different factors will be limiting at different times. Fig. 22 shows the rate of elongation of maize plants over two days.

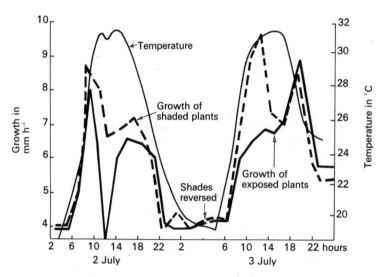

Fig. 22. Temperature and growth of maize plants in the shade and sunlight.

Give an analysis of the different environmental factors limiting growth during these two days.

2.11 Bacterial population growth

Bacteria from a culture where the population had reached the stationary phase were used to inoculate two other culture solutions. One of these culture solutions consisted of exactly similar nutrients as the original solution. The second consisted of somewhat different nutrients.

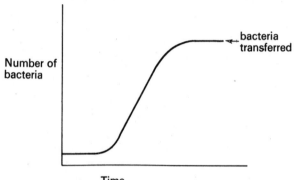

Fig. 23. Growth of bacterial population in culture.

Predict the form of the curve of population growth in each of these two solutions. Make the start of the graph the form of the curve of population growth in the original solution, shown in Fig. 23.

2.12 Continuous culture

A bacterial or yeast population will increase logarithmically until lack of food, accumulation of metabolic products or some other factor limits or inhibits the growth of the population.

Such micro-organisms which are produced commercially either for themselves (e.g. yeast) or for their by-products (e.g. lactic acid) used to be grown in batches. The culture was set up and, after a period for growth, it was harvested. A more recent method is to grow the organisms in continuous culture, enabling the product to be obtained continuously.

A piece of apparatus which could be used for continuous culture is shown in Fig. 24. After studying the diagram explain how you think the apparatus works, and how continuous production is obtained.

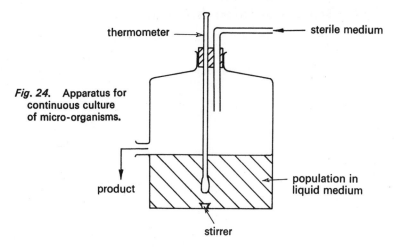

Fig. 24. Apparatus for
continuous culture
of micro-organisms.

thermometer

sterile medium

product

population in
liquid medium

stirrer

2.13   Plankton population growth

The plankton in the sea or fresh water lakes consists of both plants
(the phytoplankton) and animals (the zooplankton), some of which
feed on the phytoplankton.

Figure 25 shows the variation in numbers of phytoplankton during
one year.

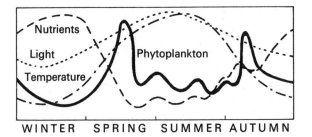

Fig. 25. Numbers of phytoplankton over one year.

1   What conditions have probably caused the large increase in numbers
of phytoplankton in spring?

2   Give a hypothesis to explain the decrease in numbers of phytoplankton during the summer, and account for the autumn rise in
numbers.

3   Speculate on the shape the curve for the growth of the zooplankton population in these conditions would take.

2.14   Growth of three different populations

Predict and draw the curves which would be obtained in each of the following cases:

1   The growth of a population of actively dividing bacteria in a small amount of nutrient medium for 48 hours.

2   The fluctuations in numbers of a population of *Drosophila* forgotten and left for 8 weeks in a closed jar containing some food.

3   The growth of a small population of rabbits over three years in a suitable area previously containing no rabbits.

3 Water Relations

3.1 The effect of external factors on the rate of transpiration

Transpiration is the loss of water vapour from plants to the air. Water evaporates from the cells into the internal air spaces, and diffuses outwards to the air, mainly through the stomata. The area of contact between the leaf cells and the internal air spaces is so great that these air spaces are usually nearly saturated with water vapour. It is, then, the rate of diffusion of water vapour through the stomata which usually determines the rate of transpiration.

1 Discuss the external physical factors which, in your opinion, will influence the rate of transpiration.

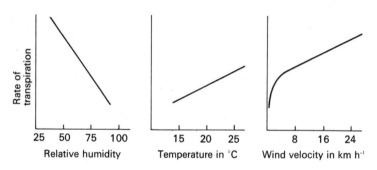

Fig. 26. Relative humidity.   *Fig. 27.* Temperature.   *Fig. 28.* Wind velocity.

Figs. 26, 27 and 28 give the effect of three external conditions on the rate of transpiration of plants.

2 Comment briefly on these graphs.

3 Would you expect the same results if, instead of a plant, a wet handkerchief had been used in these experiments?

3.2   The effect of light intensity on the rate of transpiration

Problem 3.1 dealt with the external physical factors which seem to affect the rates of transpiration and evaporation equally.   If transpiration is a purely physical, evaporative process, carried out without metabolic control, one would expect it to correspond closely with evaporation rates under various atmospheric conditions.   There are, however, internal factors in the leaf which influence the amount of water lost.   Fig. 29 compares water lost by transpiration from a leaf with that lost by evaporation from a porous pot (atmometer) during a summer's day and night.

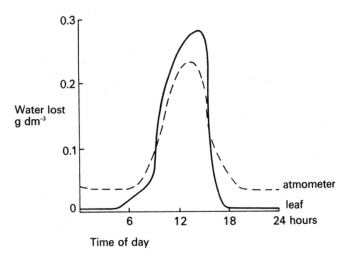

Fig. 29. Water loss from a leaf and an atmometer over 24 hours.

1   At what times during the 24 hours is transpiration less than evaporation?

2   Temperature, wind velocity, and water content of the air were the same for both leaf and atmometer.   What then seems to be the factor which affects transpiration more than it does evaporation?

Fig. 30 shows the opening and closing of stomata of *Pelargonium*.

3   Suggest a hypothesis, based on Fig. 30, to account for the difference in transpiration rates in light and dark.

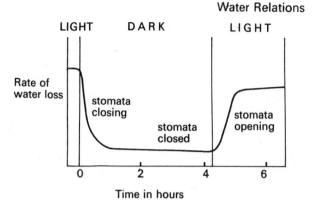

Fig. 30. Stomatal opening and closing in *Pelargonium.*

The data given in the table below incorporate a number of the factors discussed in this problem and problem 3.1. The table shows the amount of water lost by a plant related to the temperature, the light intensity and the vapour pressure deficit (VPD) of the atmosphere. (VPD is the difference between the actual vapour pressure of water in the atmosphere and the vapour pressure in an atmosphere saturated with water vapour at the same temperature.)

Time of day	Temp. °C	Light intensity (as % noon)	VPD in mmHg	Water loss $g\ m^{-2}\ h^{-1}$
02.00	18	0	6.4	10
06.00	16	0	5.6	10
08.00	16	70	5.3	30
10.00	21	100	8.4	130
12.00	29	100	22.8	270
13.00	32	100	27.5	310
14.00	34	100	31.5	280
15.00	35	100	34.3	240
16.00	34	100	31.5	170
18.00	29	0	22.8	70
20.00	22	0	7.4	12
24.00	21	0	6.7	12

WATER LOSS RELATED TO TEMPERATURE, VPD AND LIGHT INTENSITY

4 Present these results graphically in any suitable way.

5 List the conclusions which can be drawn from an interpretation of the results.

3.3   Water loss and stomatal distribution

A potometer measures the rate of water uptake by a shoot. It is, however, generally assumed during potometer experiments that the rate of water uptake is the same as the rate of water loss by transpiration. This assumption enables one to use the results from investigations as a measure of the rate of transpiration.

A leafy branch was attached to a potometer, and the rate of movement of water into the shoot measured every three minutes. After the rate had become steady the upper surfaces of the leaves were coated with vaseline to prevent water loss from that surface. The plant was left until the rate of transpiration had again become steady. The lower surfaces of the leaves were then vaselined and the new rate of transpiration measured.

Fig. 31 gives the results of the investigation.

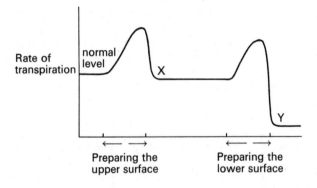

Fig. 31.   Rate of transpiration of a leafy shoot with leaves vaselined.

1   What precautions would have to be taken in the carrying out of this investigation?

2   Account for the rise in the rate of transpiration during the vaselining.

3   Suggest a hypothesis to explain the drop in the rate of transpiration at X and the larger drop at Y.

3.4   Methods of measuring transpiration

The following list gives a number of methods of measuring transpiration in plants.

Say, for each method,

a what practical precautions should be taken while measuring transpiration,

b the possible errors in the method.

1 Measure the loss in mass of a cut shoot or leaf over a short period of time.

2 Measure the loss in mass of a potted plant and its container over convenient intervals of time.

3 Measure the amount of water vapour produced by a transpiring shoot.   The plant, or part of it, is enclosed in a glass vessel through which a stream of dry air flows (Fig. 32).   The water vapour produced in transpiration is collected in tubes containing calcium chloride and weighed.   As a control the same volume of air passes through a similar apparatus with no plant.

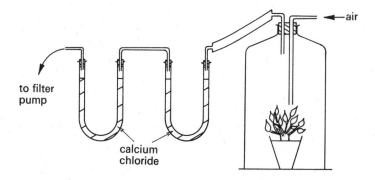

Fig. 32. Measuring transpiration by collecting water vapour from a shoot.

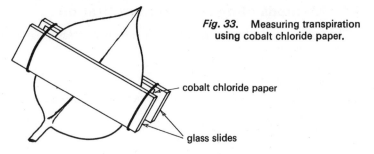

Fig. 33.   Measuring transpiration using cobalt chloride paper.

cobalt chloride paper

glass slides

4   Measure the production of water directly by absorbing it from the leaf surface.   Cobalt chloride (or cobalt thiocyanate) paper, which is blue when dry and pink when wet, is held next to the leaf surface by two pieces of glass clipped together above and below the leaf. The time taken for the paper to change from one standard colour to another shows loss of water by that part of the leaf covered.

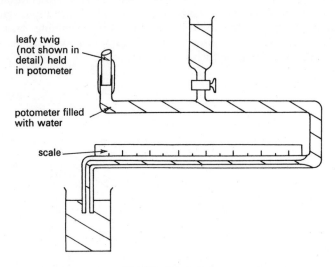

leafy twig (not shown in detail) held in potometer

potometer filled with water

scale

Fig. 34. A potometer.

5   Measure the movement of water through a cut leafy twig using a potometer.   The rate of movement of a bubble of air through the potometer is used as a measure of the rate of transpiration.   The amount of water taken in by the plant per unit time can be calculated if the bore of the tube is known.

3.5   Transpiration and water absorption

The figures shown in the table were obtained in an investigation to compare the rate of transpiration with the rate of water absorption of a plant over four-hourly periods on a summer's day.

Time	g water absorbed in 4 hours	g water transpired in 4 hours	Amount of water in leaf (as a ratio to the dry mass)	Light intensity (as % noon)
04.00	6	1	7.2	0
08.00	6	8	6.0	70
12.00	14	20	5.5	100
16.00	22	29	3.0	100
22.00	13	10	3.8.	10
24.00	8	3	7.5	0

1   Present these results graphically in any suitable way.

2   Comment on the results, particularly on the differences between the amount of water absorbed and that transpired at different times, and give possible explanations.

3.6 Xerophytic plants

A large number of plants are adapted by one means or another to tolerate occasional or even regular periods of drought. Some, notably the desert plants, can survive an incredible period of desiccation. A giant cactus, for example, kept unwatered in a laboratory for six years, lost only one third of the moisture it originally contained.

The succulents survive by storing up large amounts of water when it is available, and then conserving this water over long periods of drought, losing it only slowly. Some can also keep their stomata closed during the day, and open them at night, thus avoiding the high day-time temperatures with consequent high rate of water loss through transpiration.

Some plants, such as broom and acacia, reduce their exposure by having little or no leafage.

1 Compare the leaf of *Ammophila* (marram grass) with that of privet (Figs. 35 and 36). List those features possessed by the *Ammophila* leaf which seem to you to help in retarding water loss.

2 The seeds of a species of cactus will germinate only when they receive an uninterrupted rainfall of 2.5 cm. They will remain dormant for many years even when the total rainfall exceeds 100 cm, but does not include any continuous fall of 2.5 cm. Put forward a hypothesis based on the presence of a germination inhibitor to explain this phenomenon.

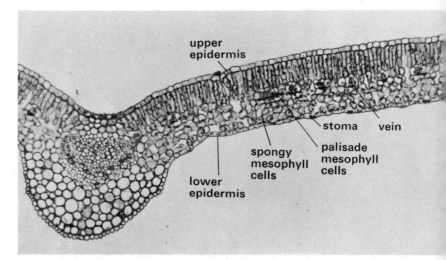

Fig. 35. T.S. privet leaf.

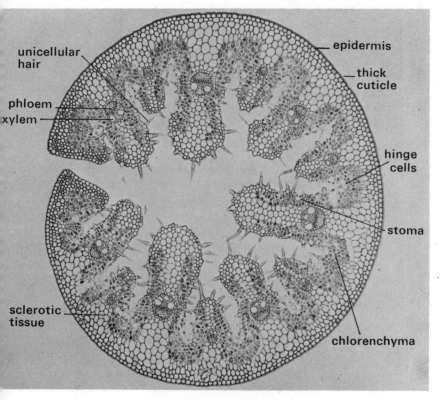

Fig. 36. T.S. *Ammophila* leaf.

3.7 Hydrophytes

Figs. 37 and 38 show some of the external and internal features of a water plant (hydrophyte), *Potamogeton*.

The plant's structure is adapted to its habitat in a number of ways. Some of these adaptations are listed below. Take each point listed and suggest how it could be an adaptation to water life.

a Filamentous habit.
b Poorly developed root system.
c Thin cuticle.
d Lack of stomata, or closed stomata, or stomata present on upper surface of floating leaves only.
e Intercellular air spaces.
f Poorly developed xylem.

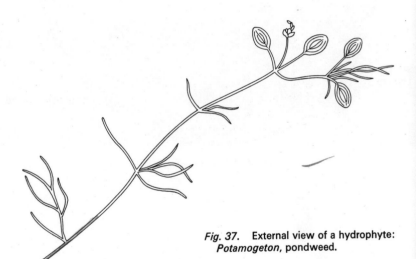

Fig. 37. External view of a hydrophyte: *Potamogeton*, pondweed.

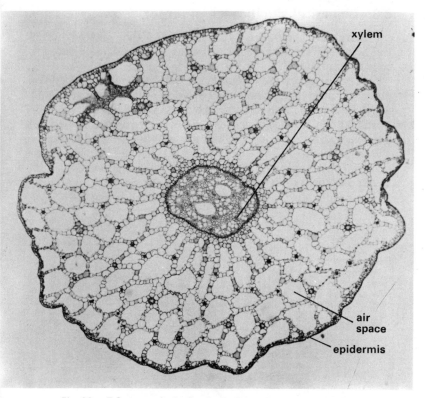

Fig. 38. T.S. stem of a hydrophyte: *Potamogeton*, pondweed.

3.8 Biological significance of turgor

When a plant's cells are fully distended the plant is said to be turgid, and no more water is taken up.   If water is lost and not replaced the cells become flaccid.

One can simulate the conditions of water loss under natural conditions by immersing tissues in a solution such as sucrose solution which is more concentrated than the cell sap (a hypertonic solution). If, in addition, a range of concentrations of the solution is used, it is possible to find the concentration of the solution which causes no change in weight or size of the tissue immersed in it.   Such a solution is said to be isotonic with the cell sap, and the water potential of this solution is equal to the water potential of the cell sap.

The results of such an investigation are given in Fig.39.

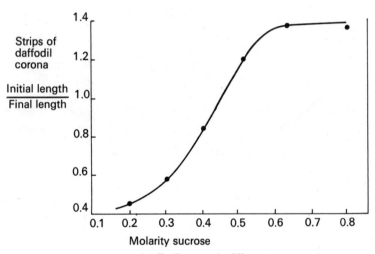

Fig. 39. Size of strips of daffodil corona in different concentrations of sucrose.

1 State

   a the molarity of the sucrose solution which is isotonic with the cell sap,

   b the water potential of the cell sap, in atmospheres (the water potential of a sucrose solution of this molarity is 12.7 atmospheres at 20 °C),

   c what is happening to cells
     i below a molarity of 0.45
     ii above a molarity of 0.45.

The turgidity of tissues immersed in such solutions can be demon-strated as follows: identical potato chips are left in (A) water (B) 20% sucrose solution.   Their appearance after 24 hours is shown in Fig. 40.

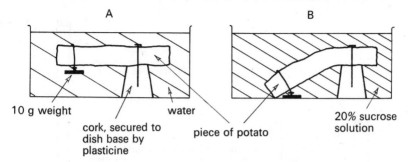

A   B

10 g weight   water
        cork, secured to   piece of potato   20% sucrose
        dish base by   solution
        plasticine

Fig. 40. Pieces of potato tuber after immersion in water and sucrose for 24 hours.

2 Which of the two is still turgid?   Explain why.

3 The aerial parts of herbaceous plants may lose water and wilt if the atmospheric conditions cause heavy loss of water by transpiration and there is no soil water available to replace the loss.   From the appearance of the chip in Fig. 40 and the wilting of plants, what con-clusions can you draw about the biological significance of turgor?

3.9 Dandelion stems

Short pieces of dandelion flower stem were partly slit in half longitudinally, and treated as shown below.

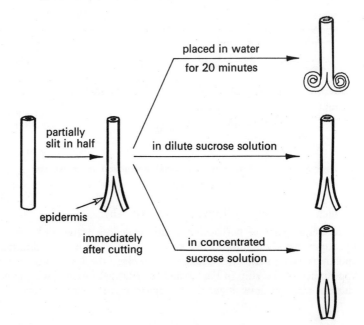

Fig. 41. Dandelion stem in sucrose solutions and water.

Suggest hypotheses to explain

1 the appearance of the stem immediately after cutting,
2 the appearance of the stem after 20 minutes immersion in water, dilute and concentrated sucrose solutions.

3.10   Ion absorption

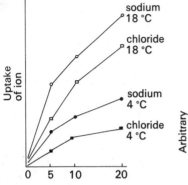
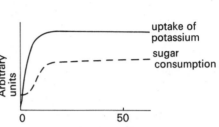

Fig. 42. Uptake of sodium chloride at two temperatures and at different concentrations of sodium chloride.

Fig. 43. Sugar consumption and uptake of potassium in different concentrations of oxygen.

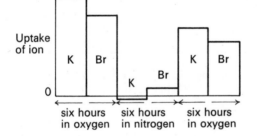

Fig. 44.   Uptake of potassium and bromide ions in air and nitrogen.

The above data are results from investigations into the absorption of ions by plants.   Combine the information given in the graphs into general statements on ion absorption by plants.   Do you think that osmosis could account for ion uptake in any of these cases?

4 Translocation

4.1 The pathway of movement for solutes in the plant

Stout and Hoagland in 1939 investigated the uptake of radioactive potassium (^{42}K) in solution by small plants of cotton, geranium and willow. The phloem and xylem in the experimental branches were separated for a length of 23 cm by delicately inserting strips of impervious wax paper between them, and then binding the branch up with paper (Fig. 45). After five hours of uptake the distribution of ^{42}K was determined by measuring the amount of radioactivity in the experimental region, and above and below it. The results are given below.

| | ppm ^{42}K | | | |
| | Branch with xylem and phloem separated | | Control branch | |
	phloem	xylem	phloem	xylem
Above stripped section	53	47	64	56
Stripped section: top	11.6	119		
middle	0.7	112	87	69
bottom	20	113		
Below stripped section	84	58	74	67

DISTRIBUTION OF ^{42}K IN WILLOW STEM

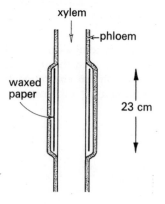

Fig. 45. Separation of xylem and phloem.

1   The control branch had been treated in order to act as a satisfactory control for the experiment. What do you think had been done to it?

2   What do the figures for the waxed strip area of the experimental branch suggest about the tissue responsible for the upward translocation of ^{42}K?

3   One would not have reached the same conclusion by an analysis of the ^{42}K in the xylem and phloem of an intact branch. One would instead have assumed that both tissues were equally responsible for the transport of potassium. In the light of the information gained from the experimental branch, how do you account for the figures for the control branch and also those above and below the waxed strip in the experimental branch?

4.2   The pathway of movement for organic materials

The transport of the radioactive isotope of phosphorus (^{32}P) was studied in a way similar to that outlined in Problem 4.1 where the xylem and phloem were separated by strips of impervious wax paper. ^{32}P was introduced into a leaf and its presence in the xylem and phloem of the stem later determined by measuring the amount of radioactivity.

The amounts of radioactive phosphorus present in experimental and control branches are shown in the table.

| | % of ^{32}P | | | |
| | Branch with xylem and phloem separated | | Control branch | |
	phloem	xylem	phloem	xylem
Top of strip	12	1	15	5
	7	trace	10	6
	13	0	5	2
Bottom of strip	5	1	3	1

DISTRIBUTION OF ^{32}P IN STEM OF COTTON

1   Are these results in accord with the hypothesis that the phloem transports organic materials produced by the leaf? Give reasons for your answer.

2   Suggest an explanation for the fact that fruit on branches which have been ringed develop extraordinarily large.

3 If a leaf is given labelled carbon dioxide ($^{14}CO_2$) during photo-synthesis, the resulting products of photosynthesis are translocated both up and down the plant. Measurements later show a greater amount of labelled carbon compounds in the tips of the shoot and root than is present in the parts of the plant between the leaf and the tips. Suggest the function of the accumulated carbon compounds.

4.3   Movement of organic substances

1 Suggest an experiment, based on the removal of rings of tissue or tissues around a branch, to see if organic substances are translocated in the phloem.

2 If organic substances are transported in the phloem, predict the outcome of such a ringing experiment done on a deciduous tree in the winter, compared with one done in the summer.

4.4   Transport in the phloem

The following statements sum up the results of a number of experiments performed in attempts to discover more about the translocation of organic materials in the phloem.

a The contents of the sieve tubes vary in relation to changes in the environmental conditions around the plant.

b Any change in the sugar content of the leaves is followed by similar changes in the sieve tube contents.

c Transport of materials stops when the phloem is killed. The rate of transport increases with increasing temperature, reaching a maximum at about 25 °C, and then falling off.

d Stems treated with a substance which inhibits respiration, or placed in an environment with no oxygen, do not transport materials in the phloem.

e Sugars can be transported both up and down the plant: young leaves, roots, and growing fruits will import sugars.

f Aphids (greenfly) feed by inserting their stylets into the phloem sieve tubes. It is possible to cut the anaesthetised body of the aphid from its stylet and collect from the cut end of the stylet the contents of the phloem (called honey-dew) on which the insect was feeding. To do this no suction need be applied. The drops of solution exude easily and quickly from the severed stylet. (Fig. 46).

Fig. 46. Drop of phloem sap exuding from the cut end of an aphid
stylet and being collected by a capillary tube. The rate of
exudation was 2μl per hour.

1 What process in the plant seems to be responsible for the formation
of the contents of the sieve tubes? Say which pieces of evidence
support your answer.

2 Is translocation in the phloem a biological or a physical process?
Say which pieces of evidence support your answer, and why they do.

3 Using the evidence given above, write a few paragraphs on the
translocation of organic substances in the plant.

4.5 Diurnal movement of xylem sap

The flow velocity of sap through the xylem of a tree was determined
in the trunk and in a small branch for a number of hours. The following data were obtained.

Time	Flow velocity of xylem sap in m h^{-1}	
	Trunk	Branch
06.00	1.0	1.1
08.00	1.1	1.4
10.00	1.4	5.3
12.00	2.7	7.8
14.00	3.2	5.9
16.00	2.7	3.9
18.00	2.1	1.8
20.00	1.6	1.3
22.00	1.4	1.3

Graph, comment on, and draw conclusions from, these findings.

4.6   Mechanism of movement up the xylem

The mechanism by which sap moves up through the xylem has long puzzled plant physiologists, and is still not fully understood. Atmospheric pressure will raise water only about 9 metres and the tallest trees known are more than ten times this height. One of the Californian redwoods (*Sequoia sempervirens*) in Humboldt County is probably the largest tree in the world. It has a height of 112 metres.

Three hypotheses have been put forward to account, in whole or in part, for this movement. They are:

a The cohesion-tension theory. Water lost in transpiration leads to the movement of water from one cell to another. The cohesion of water molecules prevents the water column breaking when subjected to the transpiration pull. As a consequence of this pull, the water in the xylem is drawn up the stem under a tension or negative pressure.

b Root pressure. The pressure exerted by the actively respiring roots taking in water from the soil also causes it to be forced upwards along a hydrostatic pressure gradient.

c Capillarity. Because of its high surface tension, water will rise in fine capillary tubes to an appreciable height. For example, in a glass tube of 0.01 mm bore water rises by capillarity to a height of about 3 metres.

Below are given a number of pieces of evidence. For each say which, if any, of the three hypotheses it supports or disproves, giving your reasons for doing so.

Then, on the basis of the evidence given, say whether you think the movement of water and salts up the xylem is a physical or a biological process.

1   When the stem of a transpiring plant is cut below the surface of a dye solution, the dye rushes in, going both up and down the stem in the xylem. Water is absorbed when poured onto the root stump of a newly felled tree.

2   If the stem mentioned in (1) is first defoliated the dye does not enter the stem.

3   The upward movement of indicator materials such as dyes or radioactive isotopes can usually be related to the rate of transpiration.

4   The cohesive or tensile strength of extracted sap measured in the laboratory varies between about 130 and 210 atmospheres.

A cohesive force of one atmosphere should support a 9.07 metres vertical column of water under ideal conditions. The tallest trees of about 90 metres would therefore require sap with a cohesive strength of about 10 atmospheres only.   If one also takes into account the forces of resistance met by the water in moving through narrow capillaries whose walls are not smooth, and the fact that these are laboratory measurements and not taken in nature, the minimum number of atmospheres theoretically required becomes more like 40.

(One atmosphere is the amount of pressure exerted by the air at sea level, and is 10^5 newtons m^{-2}.)

5   Water evaporating from a porous pot will cause a 100 cm long column of mercury to be drawn up from a reservoir below (Fig. 47). A leafy twig may be used instead of the porous pot with the same effect.

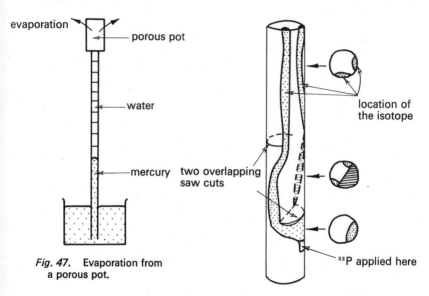

Fig. 47.   Evaporation from a porous pot.

Fig. 48.   Movement of ^{32}P around two cuts in a tree trunk.

6   The diameter of the trunk of a tree changes over 24 hours, being smallest at midday and largest at midnight.

7   In the morning water begins to move in the small branches of a tree before it does in the trunk.   The reverse is true in the evening.

8   Using the radioactive isotope of phosphorus (^{32}P) it is possible to trace the flow of sap up a tree.   When deep cuts are made into the wood directly in the path of the ascending isotope, the pathway taken avoids the cuts by moving laterally in the most recently formed xylem around them (Fig. 48).

9 Bubbles of air appear in the xylem vessels of some trees from time to time.

10 The injection of tree trunks with metabolic inhibitors and poisons causes little change in the speed at which xylem sap flows.

11 Pressures of 3 to 5 atmospheres have been recorded in investigations of root pressure. Roots in an atmosphere deficient in oxygen, or roots treated with potassium cyanide, have a very much lower pressure than normal. The root pressure is also reduced by lowering the temperature.

12 Root pressure is frequently absent in actively transpiring plants (see also point 1) and is not present in conifers and other gymnosperms.

13 The diameter of xylem elements varies from 0.01 mm (some gymnosperm tracheids) to 0.2 mm (largest vessels).

5 Respiration

5.1 Measuring respiratory quotient

The respiratory quotient (R.Q.) of a plant is the ratio of the volume of carbon dioxide given off to the volume of oxygen absorbed during respiration. It gives information about the type of substance being consumed in respiration. The equation used to calculate the R.Q. is:

$$R.Q. = \frac{\text{volume of } CO_2 \text{ produced}}{\text{volume of } O_2 \text{ absorbed}}$$

Thus the R.Q. for a carbohydrate is 1.0 as the molecules of carbon dioxide produced are equal in number to the molecules of oxygen used.

$$6O_2 + C_6H_{12}O_6 \longrightarrow 6CO_2 + 6H_2O$$

$\quad$ oxygen $\qquad$ glucose $\qquad\qquad$ carbon dioxide $\quad$ water

Fats need more oxygen than do carbohydrates for complete oxidation, so the production of carbon dioxide is less than the consumption of oxygen and the R.Q. falls below 1.0. The equation for the fat triolein is

$$C_{57}H_{104}O_6 + 80O_2 \longrightarrow 57CO_2 + 52H_2O$$

$\quad$ triolein $\qquad\quad$ oxygen $\qquad\qquad$ carbon dioxide $\quad$ water

which gives a respiratory ratio of $\dfrac{57}{80} = 0.71$

R.Q.s for the complete oxidation of respirable substances are:

fats	0.7
carbohydrates	1.0
proteins and amino acids	0.9

These values are rarely obtained in practice because there is seldom complete oxidation and, in addition, a mixture of substances may be being used in respiration. R.Q.s of 0.5 and below suggest that some of the carbon dioxide is being fixed into organic acids by the plant. Some of the *Cactaceae* and *Crassulaceae*, for example, form only malic acid and release no carbon dioxide, giving an R.Q. of 0.

R.Q.s of 2 to 7 suggest the occurrence of anaerobic respiration.

The apparatus shown in Fig. 49 may be used to measure the R.Q. Two respirometers are set up, one to measure oxygen absorption, and the other to measure carbon dioxide release.

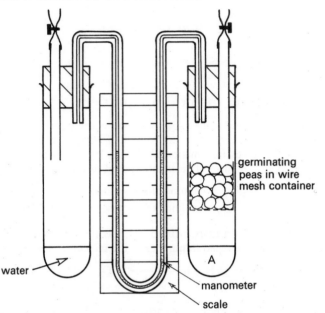

germinating peas in wire mesh container

A

water

manometer

scale

Fig. 49. A simple respirometer.

1   If A contains water, and the seeds are found to have an R.Q. of 1.0, would you expect the level of the liquid in the manometer to have changed at the end of the experiment?

2   What liquid should be in A in order to measure
   a the consumption of oxygen only,
   b the production of carbon dioxide?
   c How would you then calculate the total amount of carbon dioxide produced?

3   What control would you use for the two respirometers, and why?

4   Suggest a way of using this apparatus in order to measure the effect of temperature on the rate of respiration.

5.2   Respiratory quotients

The results given below were obtained using a respirometer similar to that described in the previous problem.

1   These figures (converted to s.t.p.) were obtained with germinating pea seeds as the respiring material.

Volume of oxygen consumed   9.3 cm^3
Volume of carbon dioxide produced *extra* to the amount
of oxygen consumed   0.9 cm^3

Calculate the R.Q.
Which type of substance is being respired?

2   The following results converted to s.t.p. were obtained with germinating castor oil seeds as the respiring material.

Volume of oxygen consumed   8.8 cm^3
Total volume of carbon dioxide produced   6.3 cm^3

Calculate the R.Q.
Which type of substance is being respired?

3   The R.Q.s of a seed and the ensuing plant are given below.   Say which substances you think are being respired.

	R.Q.
Dormant seed	0.69
Soaked seed	1.9
Young seedling with no leaves	0.99
Adult leaves	1.01

5.3   Respiratory quotient of seedlings

Fig. 50 shows the respiratory quotients obtained for seedlings from two species of plants, measured at two day intervals after the start of germination.

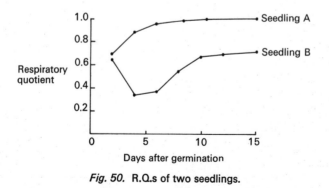

Fig. 50. R.Q.s of two seedlings.

Comment on the type of substance being used for respiration in each case.

5.4 Stored seeds

The curves in Fig. 51 give information on the storage life of wheat grain. Each point is plotted when only half the sample taken from the wheat stored under the conditions noted germinated.

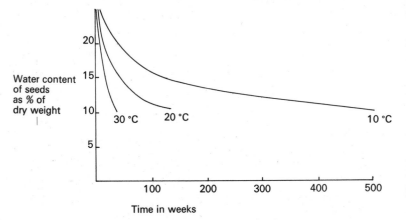

Water content of seeds as % of dry weight

Fig. 51. Storage life of wheat grain.

What would be the best way to store wheat grain in order to ensure that samples could be grown for as many years as possible? Explain the reasons for your answer.

5.5 Apple fruit growth

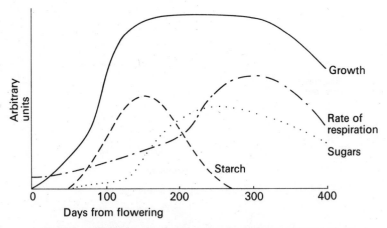

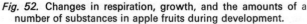

Fig. 52. Changes in respiration, growth, and the amounts of a number of substances in apple fruits during development.

Fig. 52 shows the changes in respiration, growth, and the amounts of sugars and starch found in apple fruits during their development on the tree and in storage after picking.

1 Use the graph to say when you would pick the fruit.

2 The development of a fruit such as an apple can be divided into three phases: growth, ripening, senescence. State the time in the development of the fruits shown in Fig. 52 at which you consider the last two phases to start, and say why.

3 Deduce from one of the curves on the graph two methods of storing the ripe fruit for some time after picking.

5.6 Fermentation by yeast juice

In 1905 Harden and Young discovered that fermentation by yeast juice could take place only in the presence of inorganic phosphate. They also found that this was converted into an organic form during the fermentation.

Fig. 53 summarises some of this work.

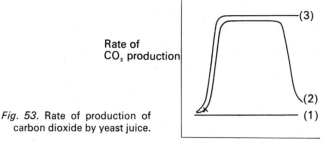

Fig. 53. Rate of production of carbon dioxide by yeast juice.

Curve (1) shows the rate of carbon dioxide production by yeast juice containing added glucose.

Curve (2) shows the rate of carbon dioxide production by yeast juice containing added glucose and with a small amount of inorganic phosphate added at X.

Curve (3) shows the same as (2), but with the addition of an enzyme which can break down organic phosphate liberating inorganic phosphate.

Interpret these graphs in the light of your knowledge of the fermentation process.

5.7   General properties of enzymes

The graphs shown in Fig. 54 give a generalised picture of various aspects of enzyme activity. All show the rate of reaction (vertical axis) plotted against an unknown factor. The four factors involved are temperature, substrate concentration, pH, enzyme concentration.

Say which graph relates to each factor, giving reasons for your answers.

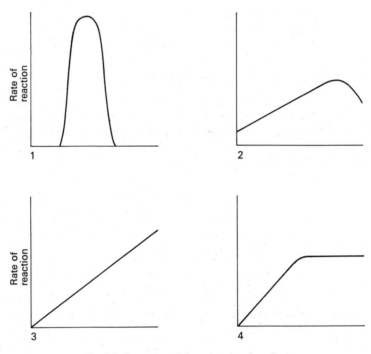

Fig. 54. Enzyme activity related to four factors.

5.8   Enzyme activity and pH

The same amount of an amylase enzyme solution was added to each of 7 test tubes containing starch solution.   The starch solution had been added to a buffer solution so that the 7 test tubes were at pHs of 4, 5, 6, 6.5, 7, 8 and 9.   Tube 8, at a pH of 6.5 had its contents boiled immediately after the enzyme had been added to the starch.

All 8 tubes were placed together in a water bath at 30 °C and left for an hour.   The contents of all tubes were then boiled.

The amount of reducing sugar in each tube was estimated, to give the comparative results shown in the table, where the amount present at pH 4 is shown as 1.

pH	4.0	5·0	6.0	6.5	7.0	8.0	9.0	boiled 6.5
Amount reducing sugar	1	12	26	32	33	27	13	0

AMOUNT OF REDUCING SUGAR FORMED BY ENZYME ACTIVITY AT DIFFERENT pH

Graph these results, and comment on them and on the procedure adopted.

6 Plant Hormones

6.1 Early work on phototropism

The following list is a summary of results from experiments performed by Charles Darwin in 1880 and biologists working in the early part of this century in an attempt to elucidate the mechanism of phototropism. A lot of the work was done on the young seedlings of oat. The organ used was the coleoptile, before the stem broke through the tip. This, and other work, produced the information that phototropism and a large number of other aspects of growth are affected by plant hormones, of which auxins are the best known. The single auxin, identified as β-indolylacetic acid (IAA), is capable of producing a number of growth effects.

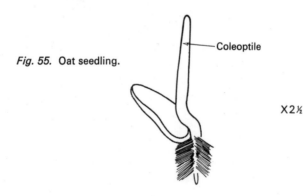

Fig. 55. Oat seedling.

Coleoptile

X2½

Summary of results

1   If the tip of the coleoptile was removed, the coleoptile did not grow. Pieces of coleoptile or stem immersed in an auxin solution elongated.

2   When illuminated from one side only, coleoptiles grew towards that side, and the bending took place a little way behind the tip.

3   If, before illumination, the tip was removed or covered by a light-proof material, the coleoptile did not grow towards the light.

4 The decapitated coleoptile would, however, grow towards the light if
  i the tip was replaced on the stump or
  ii the tip was replaced on the stump with a thin layer of gelatin between the two cut surfaces.

5 The decapitated coleoptile did not grow towards the light if cocoa butter (a fat), or mica or platinum foil was placed between the two cut surfaces instead of gelatin.

6 If the decapitated coleoptile was kept in the dark and the cut-off tip replaced at one side of the stump, the stump bent away from the side on which the tip was replaced.

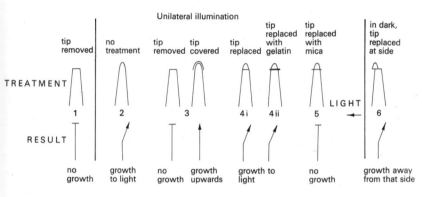

Fig. 56. Summary of results 1 to 6.

The next list summarises the conclusions which were drawn from these results.   For each conclusion say which result or results support it.

a The tip produces something which is essential for growth.
b The effect of light is *perceived* by the tip.
c The stimulus (auxin) is *produced* at the tip.
d The stimulus produced by the tip passes from there to a lower part of the coleoptile which bends.
e The stimulator substance is water soluble.
f The stimulator substance is not soluble in fat, neither is it an electric stimulus.
g A possible explanation of phototropism is that unilateral illumination causes a greater concentration of the growth stimulating substance on the darker side of the coleoptile.   This causes greater growth on that side, with consequent bending towards the light.

6.2 Phototropism

When the coleoptiles of oat seedlings which have been germinated and grown initially in the dark, are illuminated by light from one side only, further growth takes place in such a way that the tips of the coleoptiles grow towards the light.

Two hypotheses were put forward to explain this behaviour:

(1) De Candolle's hypothesis: phototropism results from a reduction of growth on the side nearest the light source, that is, a response to the *intensity* of light.

(2) Sach's hypothesis: phototropism is a response to the actual *direction* of the light, that is, the direction in which the light rays penetrate the plant.

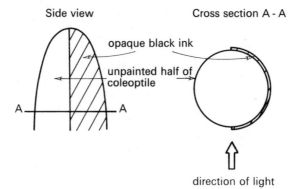

The coleoptile is painted so that half of the side near the light source, and half of the side away from the light source, are shielded by ink

Fig. 57. Unilateral light on a painted coleoptile.

1 If an experiment is set up as shown in Fig. 57, in what direction would you predict growth on the basis of
  i hypothesis 1
  ii hypothesis 2?

2 In fact the coleoptiles grew as shown in Fig. 58. They bent towards the light source, but deviated strongly towards the unpainted side. What conclusion can you draw from this result?

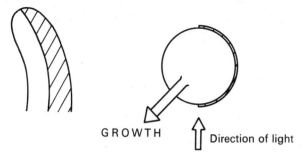

GROWTH   Direction of light

Fig. 58. Reaction of painted coleoptile to unilateral light.

6.3   Geotropism in roots

The following list is a summary of results from the early classical work on geotropism in roots.

1   When the root was placed horizontally, it grew towards gravity. The bending took place just behind the tip.

2   If the tip was removed, the root
   i no longer responded to gravity,
   ii continued to elongate.

3   If the tip was replaced on a decapitated root, the root
   i responded to gravity, and
   ii had a lower growth rate than it had without the tip.

4   A coleoptile tip on a decapitated root also retarded growth.

5   Root tips placed at one side on decapitated coleoptiles caused a positive curvature (as when the coleoptile's own tip is replaced at one side).

6   Agar blocks containing IAA (an auxin) when placed on decapitated roots caused
   i a retardation of growth if placed on straight and
   ii a negative curvature if placed at one side (i.e. a curve towards the side on which the block was placed), as also did the one-sided replacement of root tips.

7   Very low concentrations of IAA applied to decapitated roots led to an acceleration of growth.

8   There was more auxin in the lower half of horizontally placed roots than in the upper.

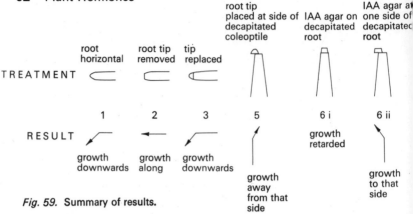

Fig. 59. Summary of results.

The next list summarises the conclusions which were drawn from these results.   For each conclusion say which result or results support it.

a The effect of gravity is *perceived* by the tip.
b The auxin is *produced* at the tip.
c The stimulus perceived by the tip passes from there to the area behind the tip which bends.
d The auxin of both root and shoot is the same, or has similar effects.
e The auxin produced at the root tip retards root growth.
f The auxin produced at the root tip stimulates coleoptile growth.
g Increasing the auxin level, or even bringing it up to its normal value for roots, retards root growth.
h Very low concentrations of IAA accelerate root growth.
i The root is more sensitive to auxin than is the stem.

6.4   Auxins in stem and root

β-indolylacetic acid is an auxin which can be manufactured artificially.   Its effects, when applied at different concentrations to a plant, can be measured accurately.

Fig. 60 shows the growth responses of roots and stems to varying concentrations of externally applied auxin.

1   Both root and stem have a range of auxin concentration which promotes growth and a range which inhibits growth.   Which organ is the more sensitive to auxin?

2   Describe in words the effect of auxin on the growth of

a the stem,   b the root.

3   Externally applied auxin is absorbed more readily by dicotyledons than by monocotyledons.   Suggest a use to which this property can be put.

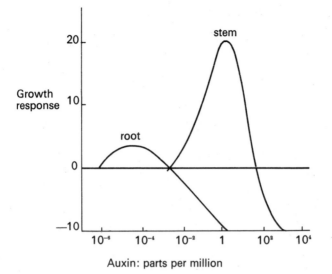

Fig. 60. Root and stem response to applied auxin.

6.5 Geotropism

Fig. 61 illustrates geotropism in a seedling. The region which produced the auxin is shaded. When the seedling is turned horizontally (as in *b*) auxin accumulates on the lower side. Fig. 1*c* shows the response of root and shoot to the horizontal position.

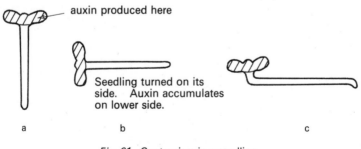

Fig. 61. Geotropism in a seedling.

Give a hypothesis, based on the different effects auxin has on the growth of roots and shoots, to explain the opposite geotropic responses of typical roots and shoots.

6.6 Transport of auxin

Figs. 62 and 63 give details of experiments on auxin transport in stems.

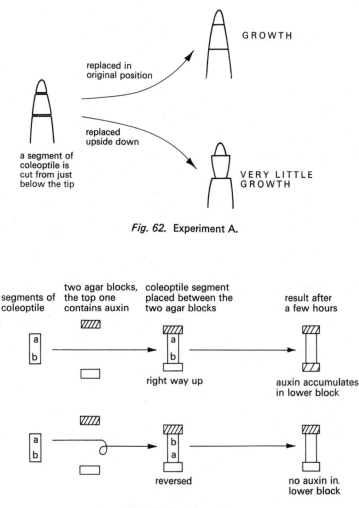

Fig. 62. Experiment A.

Fig. 63. Experiment B.

1 What was the hypothesis under investigation?
2 What conclusion may be drawn from these two experiments?

6.7   Buds and auxins

Fig. 64 shows treatment given to a shoot bearing a large terminal bud and a number of lateral buds.

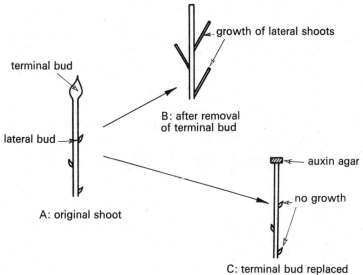

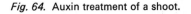

Fig. 64. Auxin treatment of a shoot.

1   Put forward a hypothesis to explain the results shown.

2   If your hypothesis is correct what would you expect to happen to the decapitated shoot if an agar block containing no auxin were placed on the tip?

3   How can this phenomenon be exploited when growing plants commercially?

6.8 Auxin and fruit development

Auxins are found in other plant organs besides roots and shoots, and have many other functions besides those of accelerating and retarding growth. One of these functions concerns the abscission of plant organs. The data given here are concerned with one such organ: a fruit.

The level of auxin in the developing fruit of apple varies during the period of development in the way shown in Fig. 65. Also shown in Fig. 65 is the amount of fruit drop at different times during development. Fig. 66 shows a section across an oddly shaped apple.

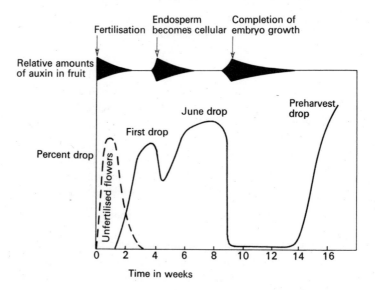

Fig. 65. Auxin production and fruit drop in apple.

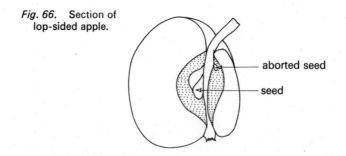

Fig. 66. Section of lop-sided apple.

Comment on

1   the relationship between auxin level and fruit drop

2   the relationship between seed growth and fruit growth

3   within the developing fruit, the possible source of each burst of
     auxin

4   the implications of this information for apple fruit growing.

6.9   The development of strawberries

The strawberry fruit consists of a swollen red receptacle, with a
large number of small fruits (achenes) embedded in it.

Fig. 67 shows ripe strawberry fruits which have been treated as
described under each diagram.

A. Untreated. The receptacle
    is swollen and red, and
    achenes are scattered over it.

B. Achenes removed at the
    tip of the fruit before
    development.

C. All achenes removed
    before development.

D. All achenes removed.
    Replaced by auxin-
    containing paste

Fig. 67. Strawberries.

Comment on the relationship between seed, auxin and fruit growth.

6.10   The effect of plant growth substances on fruit set

An investigation into the effect of growth substances on fruit set involved pears as the experimental fruit.   A number of varieties of pear produce a lot of blossom but do not set fruit successfully.   In this investigation the growth substance, gibberellic acid (GA), in lanolin was applied to the flowers of several varieties of pear.   Some control flowers were treated with lanolin only, and some were untreated. The number of fruits still on the tree was counted at intervals.

The table below gives the results for three treatments as a percentage of the flowers treated; and also the mass of the fruits at harvest.   The results are given as a means of all varieties.

Treatment	Percentage of treated flowers remaining on the tree				Mass of fruit at harvest (g)
	June 1st	June 21st	Aug. 10th	Sept. harvest	
Untreated	66	8	1	1	63
Lanolin only	48	18	1	1	48
GA in lanolin	66	25	21	20	35

NUMBER AND MASS OF PEAR FRUITS AFTER AUXIN TREATMENT

Comment on these results.